amra and the living water

John 4:1-42 FOR CHILDREN

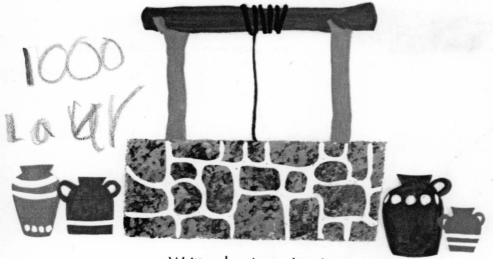

Written by Anne Jennings

Illustrated by John D. Firestone & Associates

COPYRIGHT © 1976 CONCORDIA PUBLISHING HOUSE, ST. LOUIS, MISSOURI

MANUFACTURED IN THE UNITED STATES OF AMERICA

ALL RIGHTS RESERVED

ISBN 0-570-06100-8

Publishing House
St. Louis

ARCH Books

Twelve-year-old Amrah told her guest,
Who listened eagerly:
"I wish so much that you had been
With Mother and with me

Five years ago, here at the well.
I have the strangest tale to tell.
We hurried to the water's edge.
The Man was seated on the ledge."

"What Man?" asked Mirah, also twelve.
"Oh, Jesus was His name.
His face was beautiful and kind,
Each eye, a gentle flame.

His voice was music, full and round.
It had a deep and bell-like sound.
His smile was like the setting sun,
All glowing when the day is done."

"What did he want?" asked Mirah then.
"Some water for a drink.
My mother answered, 'It is strange,
This wish of yours, I think.
For you are of Jewish clan,
While I am a Samaritan.
There is no love lost, it is true,
Between Samaritan and Jew.'"

"What did He say?" young Mirah asked.
"I never shall forget
The words He spoke!" her friend replied.
"Why, I can hear them yet!

'One drinks from this old well and then
Most certainly will thirst again.
Who takes the water I shall give
Will never thirst, but gladly live!' "

"What is this water?" Mirah asked.
"I do not understand."
"The water of lasting faith
That comes at God's command.
'Give me this drink,' cried Mother then,
'That I may never thirst again!'
'Go fetch your husband here,' said He.
'I have no husband,' answered she.

" 'You have been married more than once,
O woman!' He declared.
Quite dazed that He should know so much,
My mother sat and stared.

'Each day Christ's coming nearer brings,'
She said at last. 'He knows all things.
He's the Messiah, You'll agree.'
Then Jesus answered, 'I am He.'

"My mother gazed in wonderment
And put her pitcher down,
Then took my hand and sped with me
Straight to the nearby town.

She cried, 'At Jacob's well is One
Who knows all that I've ever done
And doubtless some things I forgot.
He's the Messiah, is He not?'

"My mother looked so beautiful.
Her eyes were lamps aglow.
While she was talking of the Man,
Her voice was soft and low.
'He's the Messiah, and He brings
Us happiness. He knows all things.
He loves God's creatures, great and small;
And surely He will save us all.'

"She was so earnest," Amrah said,
"As she was talking there.
The people listened quietly.
The birds hung in the air.

The little breezes scarcely stirred,
As if they would not miss a word.
My mother finished, led the way
Back to the well that wondrous day."

"What happened next?" young Mirah asked.
"I'm very much excited!"
"The people sought the Stranger out,
And then they all invited
Him to remain, explain God's ways.
He did just that for two whole days.
They stayed, His teachings to receive,
Then said to Mother, 'We believe.'"

"I'm glad you've told me all these things."
Said Mirah thoughtfully.
"Since I have been your houseguest here,
Some things have puzzled me.

The beggar boy your mother fed
On goat's milk and some barley bread
Was much surprised to learn, I think,
Of 'living water' for his drink.

"I'll speak to her," said Mirah then,
"Just as I talk to you.
Perhaps she'll show me how to get
Some 'living water' too.

I hope she'll share her thoughts with me;
Each one a silver thread shall be.
I'll study it, all shining bright,
And then I'll let it be my light."